ARABESQUE DESIGNS
COLORING BOOK

J. BOURGOIN AND
NICK CROSSLING

DOVER PUBLICATIONS, INC.
MINEOLA, NEW YORK

Bibliographical Note

Arabesque Designs Coloring Book, first published by Dover Publications, Inc., in 2015, contains all the plates from the following previously published Dover books: *Arabic Patterns Coloring Book* by J. Bourgoin (designs 1–31) and *Arabesque Designs Coloring Book* by Nick Crossling (designs 32–63).

This 2015 edition published by Dover Publications, Inc., for Barnes and Noble, Inc.

International Standard Book Number
ISBN-13: 978-0-486-80752-2

Manufactured in the United States by RR Donnelley

9

1

4

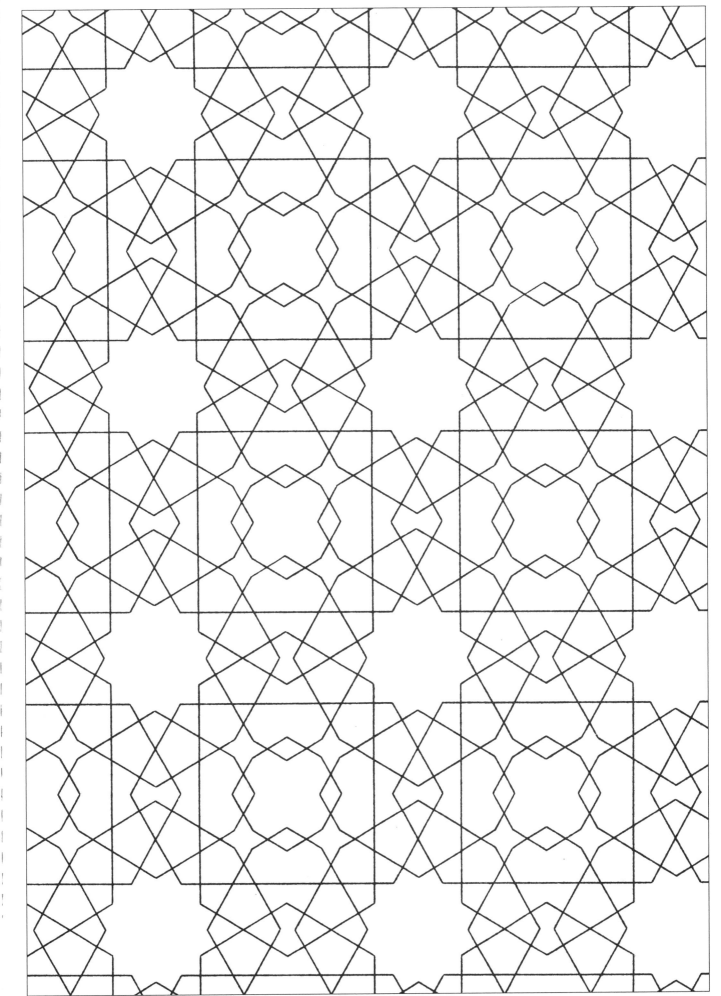

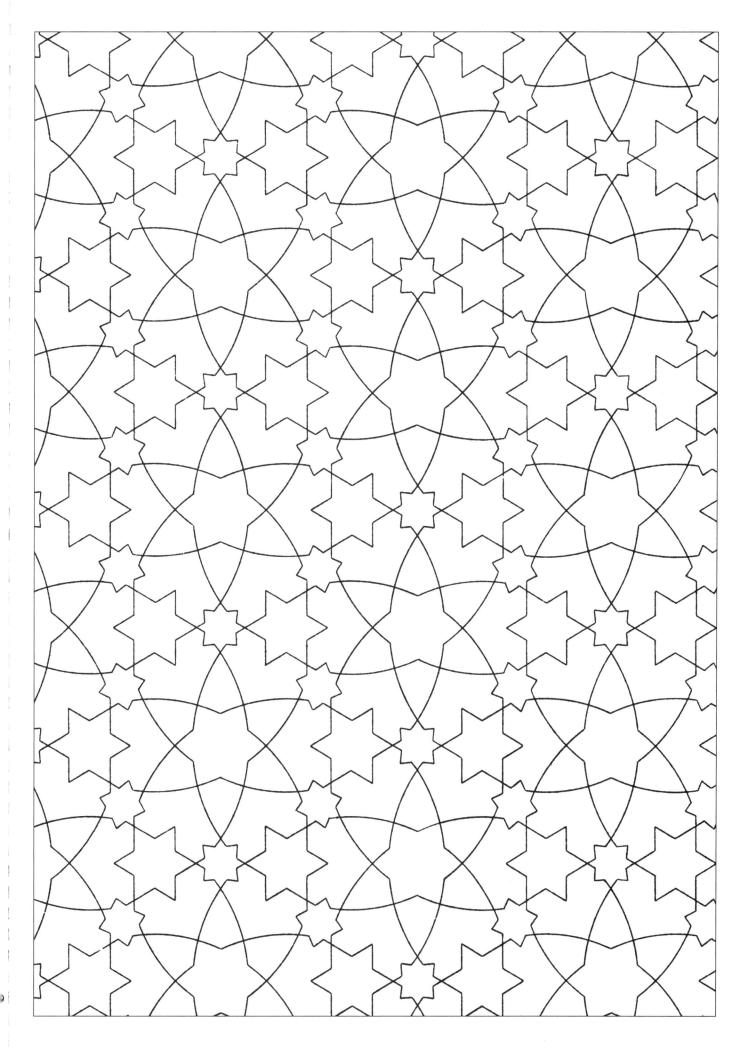

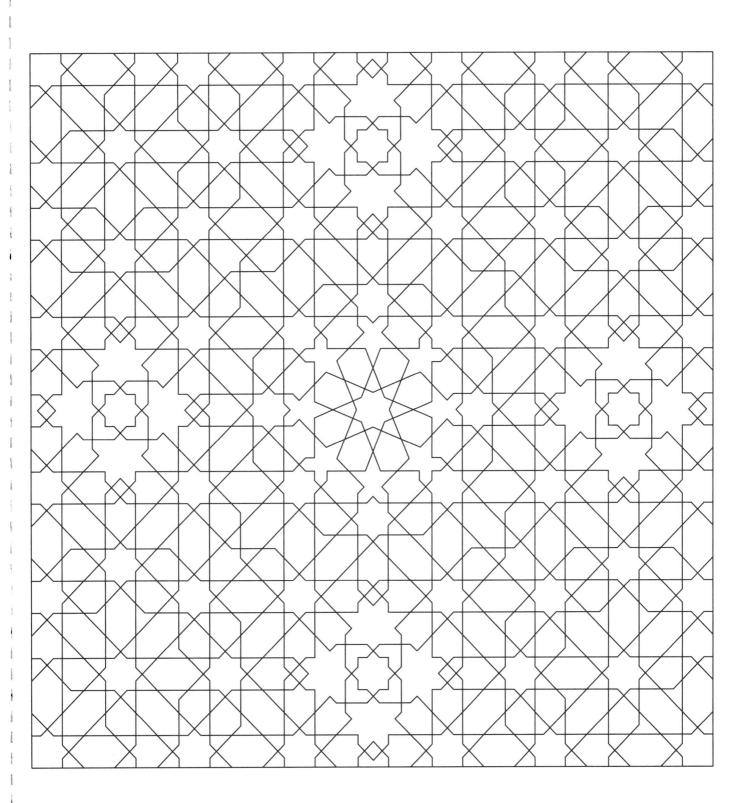

1